THE REMAINS OF LOGAN DANKWORTH

Luke Wright is a poet and theatre-maker. Flamboyant, political and riotously funny, Wright's inventive spoken word shows are enjoyed by thousands of people across the world every year. He is the author of two full poetry collections, three pamphlets and two previous verse plays. He is the winner of a Fringe First, a Stage Award and two Saboteur Awards. He lives in Suffolk with his two sons and a gnawing sense of inadequacy.

ALSO BY LUKE WRIGHT

POETRY

The Toll (Penned in the Margins, 2017)
Mondeo Man (Penned in the Margins, 2013)
The Vile Ascent of Lucien Gore (Nasty Little Press, 2011)
High Performance (Nasty Little Press, 2009)

VERSE DRAMA

Frankie Vah (Penned in the Margins, 2018)
What I Learned from Johnny Bevan (Penned in the Margins, 2016)

NON-FICTION

Who Writes This Crap? (Penguin, 2007)

The Remains of Logan Dankworth

Luke Wright

Penned in the Margins

LONDON

PUBLISHED BY PENNED IN THE MARGINS
Toynbee Studios, 28 Commercial Street, London E1 6AB
www.pennedinthemargins.co.uk

First published 2020

Printed in the United Kingdom by CPI Group

ISBN
978-1-908058-69-0

ACKNOWLEDGEMENTS

Thanks are due to the commissioners of this piece: Norwich Arts Centre, Freedom Festival, National Centre for Writing and Colchester Arts Centre. I also gratefully acknowledge the receipt of a grant from Arts Council England.

I am grateful for edits from Alex Thorpe (director), Sarah Dickenson (dramaturg) and Tom Chivers at Penned in the Margins. Alex and Sarah were part of the brilliant team of artists who worked with me to create the first production of this play, a team also including Polly Wright (composer) and Joe 'Lamps' Price (lighting design). I particularly want to thank Alex, who did so much to bring this work up to scratch.

Thanks also to Martin Rowson, Steve Forster and Molly Naylor for their early feedback, and to Liz Downie, Suba Das and all at HighTide for their continued support.

Thank you to my family: Sam, Aidan, Rosy and Olive. I love you.

Finally, this play was first performed at Norwich Arts Centre on 13th November 2019. I'd like to thank all the excellent staff there and dedicate this book to Norwich Arts Centre's director Pasco-Q Kevlin. Pasco works tirelessly everyday to support artists like me. They should fucking knight him.

for Q

THE Remains
OF Logan
Dankworth

AND SO I'm on The Green.
You'll know the place;
it's opposite The Houses of Parliament.
It's where reporters film their links
and drab fanatics make their year-round protests.

I love it here.
When I first moved to London, twenty-one and skint,
I took to tramping all across the city.
Westminster was like a real-life film set.
I'd stop and stare across the tops of taxis,
try to take it in —
the seat of British power.
In there, I thought,
in there, the lives of Britons everywhere
can change for ill or good.

There are people who will tell you
that the building's neo-Gothic trash,
Victorian and fake, a front
pretending it's much grander than it is.

But don't we all do that?

This building is a gaudy, gilt-rimmed mirror,
pocked with black spots —
reflecting us back at ourselves.

Imperfect like democracy,
in hock to charming devilry,
but underneath that ceremony
something human, something good,
where commoners can come from every corner,
represent their kin and fight for them —
to me this is the centre of the world.

So, I'm on The Green,
walking from a meeting to a meeting,
headphones on,
November 2015,
when I check my phone
and there it is —
the email I'd been waiting for.

I click it shut.
If it is a 'no'
I can carry on,

freelancing, chipping in,
sniping from the sidelines.

But if it is a 'yes'
it is my ticket to the frontline
and I can just feel the times
fizzing all around me:
Corbyn (Corbyn!) leading Labour,
Tories in for real this time,
an EU referendum on the way.

I used to watch the footage of the Berlin Wall,
the Soviets all marching with their bomb,
Spitting Image,
Tiananmen Square,
and I'd long for it.

I believed that Fukuyama line:
the end of history.
I'd lived through it,
unawares at after-school clubs,
gaga with my grandparents at Disneyland.

And when I came of age
the worst we had was Blair.
We made a show of hating him.
We walked the London streets that day in February
and gathered in the park,
but nothing had that sense of danger —
not for me.
I wanted to be part of history.

And history didn't end, did it?
It just passed out,
wasted on the eighties.
But history is stirring now,
slapping the alarm clock,
hacking up its lungs,
falling out of bed,
coffee on and ciggie on the back step,
plotting, scheming.

And I can be in the middle of it all —
a weekly column for *The Pugilist*,
that is what the email is about,
a weekly column

crying foul in prose that sings and scorches,
taking tyranny to task on Twitter,
being heard.

And I got the job.
I'd only gone and done it. Yes!

My instinct is to swipe then tap on Megan's number,
let it ring and ring and ring and ring,
imagining her squeals down the phone
and our daughter singing,
"Well done Daddy"...

§

I first met Megan at a Stop the War event,
my early days of stand-up,
March '04,
some village hall with flags and banners heavy on the walls,
a gathering of mustard-fingered comrades
who'd seen it all before
and earnest students types
converted to the cause by Tony's war.

I used to ham my Essex up on stage.
I've got a little twang of it
from growing up near Maldon,
a little bit of salt tongue from the Blackwater,
but not enough to hide my urbane roots.
My father worked in offices, my mother
stayed at home; my consonants are from the shelves
of Waitrose, my vowels from column inches
in *The Times*, and echoed off the flagstones
of my good school.

And these just didn't fit
this new zeal in my chest
and so I glottal stopped and dropped my aitches.
I let the Rs intrude upon my set.

And afterwards, half-leaning on the bar,
she sought me out
with thick black hair,
six-foot tall in flat shoes
and a thrilling frankness in her grey-green eyes.

I fancied her like *that*
and she destroyed me.
"You're kinda funny, but
you're putting on that voice.
Like, you're giving it *all of that*.
Oh my God! Are you Ray Winstone?
Are you actual Ray Winstone?
Oh! No, you're not now you're not on stage!

I'm from Essex too.
What school you go to then?"

"All right then, I admit it, I'm a bit posh."

She smiled at me so sweetly then.
Did she feel bad
that I had shrunk so easily beneath her gaze?
She took her pint of cider and
her bag of Ready Salted Walkers
then she left, a quick look back to say,

"And no one minds!"

It turned out she was right.
And it was real love for me;
the fact that she had challenged me
had changed me.
I fantasised about a life together
in which we lived our truth.

And ten years down the line
we have that life.

Back on the Green
the phone rings and rings and rings and

*"Hello... Got what..? I thought you already had... Well done... Yes,
you're very clever. What time you back?... What? Now? Oh Logan,
for fuck's sake... I thought you'd be back any minute, she's been a
nightmare today... Yeah, alright, alright... Yeah, I love you too."*

§

A month goes by.
We're under separate blankets on the sofa,
snapping squares of chocolate

and sipping cans of cider.
This is what passes for intimacy
most evenings in our Peckham flat.
We double-screen the fag end of a box set,
mop up bits of work
and wrangle with the Rubik's cube
of our shared calendar.

We're exhausted — our daughter Suzy's three —
and she was late to wean, to walk, to talk,
and even now she has us up at night.
We watch the other toddlers doing things
our little girl cannot,
stay silent as the other mums and dads swap notes
and do their observational routines
in which we miss the jokes.

I feel like I am well across my brief.
The modern father —
nappies, night feeds, rhyme time, stories,
playgroups with the other dads,
our partners on their tip-toes back to work.

It isn't just for show, you know.
I'm not the sort of man who only cooks for guests.
(You know the type I mean,
who does an Ottolenghi
and uses every pan,
soaks up all the praise
then leaves it to *the missus* on a weeknight.)

But I earn more than her
so it makes sense for me to work.
We both agreed to split it 60/40,
sometimes more.

Megan puts her phone back down
and turns the telly off.

"I've got some news...
I should have said.
But then you were away.
I didn't want to jinx it.
It's a job...
it's really good, Logan.
It's Head of Campaigns.

The charity is fucking brilliant.
It's all about community cohesion.
It's so up my street,
but —
it's full-time."

Our eyes meet in the silence,
all her frankness.
She tucks a strand of hair behind her ear,
a move I know so well;
she glances nervously from me
then to her slipper, from me
then to her slipper, me again.

The last three years have stomped on us,
raged screaming through our tidy life,
upturning shelves and smashing all our things;
it barely stopped
and we began to fight each other
for what little silence still remained.

But as I watch her pick her slipper's sole
I love her so completely.

I want to wrap her up and stroke her head
to make it all ok,
and then it hits me that I can.
Relief like lukewarm water trickles through me.

"Yes! It's ok love, it's fine, we'll make it work."

And I can tell I've knocked her off guard.
She smiles at me; it's genuine and huge
and I am loving this!

We gabble at each other
blow a bubble up around our heads with plans:
"Increase her time at nursery."
                                    "She'll benefit from it."
"Yeah, it's what she needs."
                    "I'll do less gigs, I've got the column now."

She looks at me, I'm truly on her side:
"There's something else...
The job, it's in Southend."

"What, in Essex?!
Rather you than me.
What's that, an hour on the train?"

She winces:
"Look, it's been a shitty year.
This flat's too small for us.
It costs too much.
Our friends are moving on..."

She trails off and reaches for her phone.
I watch the thing come nearer,
bearing Rightmove on its screen,
and now the dreadful truth of it comes dawning,
wailing, cold-sweat, two-tone klaxon:
Megan scrolling red-brick Essex semis.
"Look what we can get in Southend, babes."

Is she for real?
The silence that ensues screams at me.
"Just one thing at a time, eh love?"

§

I'm working on my second column for *The Pugilist*.
I'm fucking stressed.
My editor, Lucas Sergeant, is on the phone:
"It needs to be more fighty, yeah?
I need some pull quotes, Logan."

Behind me I hear Suzy talking with her dolls.
I should have got this all done yesterday
when Suzy was in nursery.
I mean, I did,
I got it done,
it's just that Lucas wants it done again.

"It's complicated though," I say.
"TTIP is this corporate charter
but leaving Europe will
eradicate the rights of workers..."

"All right, Kier fucking Hardie,
if it's all a shit show, say so,
just make it funny.
You're a stand-up who knows a bit about politics —
we don't pay you for analysis.

I need you for the clicks.
Be outrageous, yeah?
The nastier the better.
And I need this in an hour." CLICK.

I knead my throbbing temples with my thumbs;
if I don't sort this out he'll sack me,
and then she'll say, *Oh never mind,*
we can make a new start in Southend.
She's ramping up the pressure now,
an endless stream of links to houses on identikit estates.
They look like fucking satire.
I slap my hands flat on the table,
groan-growl to the ceiling.

"Shh... Daddy quiet!"
Suzy's quoting chunks of *PAW Patrol*,
both sides of the conversation,
does the dialogue really well.
I sit beside her, listen to her back-and-forth.
It's giving me a thought!

"You clever girl!"

She takes my hand in both of hers —
it's monstrous on her on tiny fingers —
kisses it so carefully
then carries on her dialogue.
It's brilliant!
It fires me up.
I kiss her back.
I breath her in
then pad back to the table with a plan.

§

"She wants to move to fucking where?"
Lucas Sergeant sits across from me
in Black Lane Coffee Co.,
my favourite coffee shop:
Australian baristas
— tattoos, beards and barber's aprons —
brewing coffee over bunsen burners,
all served up in a chemistry flask.
The coffee is, as Lucas says,

"Tip-fucking-top."

He drains his paper cup
and turns it in his clammy ham-hands for a moment.

"Southend's a fucking shithole, Logan.
Practically the countryside!
No doubt you'll write some nauseating memoir,
full of glutinous descriptions of the pastoral,
and tell us how wild swimming helped conquer your anxiety,
or maybe you could be our UKIP correspondent.
Jokes, you prick.
We don't have a UKIP correspondent —
we're not the Express."

"Anyway...
everyone, it seems, is very pleased with you.
Even Bella says,
He walks the perfect line between sensational and serious.
So who's clever boy then."
I bow my head and spread my arms dramatically.

"And this blog's a fucking godsend."
I knew the blog was coming.
I know all about the blog.

"Someone fucking hates you mate!
No inkling who it is?
Dankworth's Valet."
He gets it on his phone.
"Dankworth's Valet!"

The blog that he's referring to
is dedicated to debunking ever column that I write.
The whole thing — just on me!

But what he doesn't realise is:
I'm the one who's writing it.

"So the joke is that it's written by your servant?
Oh drop the act, as if you haven't read the thing.
I bet you check it every day.
Take it as a compliment.
It seems that you can't fart without him criticising you.
Dankworth's Valet. Dankworth's Valet!
He's got you bang to rights."
Lucas wrinkles up his nose,
inspects the ceiling, sniffs
and whispers to himself approvingly:

"Dankworth's Valet.
Yeah, it's fucking war out there."

I drain the last dregs from my cup.
"But we're the good guys, right?"

He pulls a face,
as if he's never thought of that,
and then his phone vibrates.
"Oh, here he comes."
I shuffle round to watch as David Cameron
sidles to the podium in Downing Street,
his fat face sallow,
visibly exhausted.

On Monday I will commence the process set out under our
Referendum Act. And I will go to Parliament and propose that
the British people decide our future in Europe through an in-out
referendum on Thursday 23rd June. The choice is in your hands.

"The choice is in my hands!"
Lucas throws his arms up to the ceiling.
"Now we're on.

Now the real fighting starts."
I sagely nod and savour it,
a tiny whiff of history in the air.

§

Suzy has a pre-school music group
on Tuesday afternoons.
Megan's on a half-day and she plans to meet us there
but first we've twenty fractious minutes on the bus
and Suzy only wants to see my phone.

I filed yesterday
a thousand words of top-notch Boris bashing.
He's come out for the other side.
It's clear he's only doing it to win the Tory base —
as if they'll ever make him PM.

"Who that man?" she asks me,
jabbing at the grim peroxide thatch
and accidentally liking one of Katy Hopkins' tweets.

"He's just a man, a politician."

She shrugs and turns back to the window.
"And a cunt."

My valet's blog was nasty yesterday.
He called my Boris bashing hypocritical —
As if he isn't privileged!
Dankworth runs his household like a sweat shop.
Mr Johnson, I implore you, please employ me.
Casting Boris and his chums
as natural comrades of the working class
and smearing me and my like
as the bland consumerists who don't belong —
all "Let's-all-move-to" housing porn
and live streams of the latest iPhone launch.

And Twitter is alight with it today;
it pings and pings.
Some take my side and some take his
but one thing is for sure:
I'm being heard.

Suzy chats away and pulls my arm
as I make vain attempts to jab the screen.

She barely said a word till she was three.
It panics you
when Rob and Sarah call and coo,
Oh Hector's reading now,
and Suzy's sat there bashing blocks together.
Mute.

Before they talk they seem so wise —
enormous eyes, sat gazing up at you.
What are you thinking, Suzy?
What secrets do you know?
What rich and complex thoughts possess my daughter?

It's colourful and welcoming in the church hall —
cushions on the floor
and little xylophones and drums laid out.
But Suzy limpets to my leg;
she doesn't like the echo
and her hands shoot to her ears.

"She's just a little sensitive," I say
as I meet Kate —
dungarees, retroussé nose

and *Dig for Victory* headscarf.

She cocks her hip and locks her chubby baby to her side.
"Oh my god, are you Logan Dankworth?
I love your column, so funny.
That thing about Boris!
It's so cool that you do this
and you... write."
It's thrilling to be recognised like this.

And so, the session starts.
"Let's go sit down," I say to Suzy,
who's resistant to the move.
She pulls her hand away:
"No, Daddy. Stop! I don't like it."
I gently coax her, conscious of my audience,
but when she finally comes with me,
she curls up in my lap.

The other kids all sing the songs
but Suzy won't join in.
It's stressing me out.
A sailor went to sea sea sea —

I join in too emphatically,
clapping like a lunatic,
joshing Suzy on.

A sailor went to sea sea sea, I sing all fakey-fun,
as Suzy's hands swoosh to her ears again.
I take them and I try to make them clap.
She pulls away from me and runs across the room.
I'm blushing as I haul my creaking frame back up,
to see what he could see see see,
"Come on, Suzy, let's join in!"
I try to pick her up but she starts screaming,
kicking out at me,
but all that he could see see see,
and now the other parents turn to stare.
Kate offers me a smile in solidarity.
I try to look unflustered
so I wave
then Suzy bites my forearm
and I drop her.

She slaps the parquet floor.
That sickening silent second sucks the breath from me.

The room is frozen.
Then she howls like an animal.
It's horrible
and everyone is crowding us.
I'm holding her, her tiny fragile body.
Sorry, sorry, sorry.
I feel the other parents judging me.
Imagine Kate recounting this to friends:
Yeah, met him once, really intense guy.
Not good. Horrible to his child.

I pick her up
and take her to the lobby for some air.
We sit there, slumped-defeated,
as the wheels on the bus go round and round
and round and round next door.
Megan finds us in this stasis, breathing.

"Sorry I just couldn't get away.
This fella we've been helping...
then the train was cancelled...
Woah! What happened here?"

She stoops and kisses Suzy on the forehead —
an *Evening Standard* in her hand
with Boris Johnson on the front
and Suzy, sweetly, lifts her head
and points at him:
"Cunt."

§

I'm on the ragged edge through Spring.
It's like I'm doing everything.
I'm blasting through my work
and keeping calm when Suzy takes
her boots off in the street
or puts my iPhone down the loo
and Megan misses dinner times.
I'm holding us together,
showing Megan this *can* work
if only we could find our rhythm.

And I don't want to spend my days like this
'cause history is blooming in our midst
as bar rooms bounce like boxing rings.

From Sennen up to Thurso,
from Aber through to Yarmouth,
blokes are tooled up with opinions
that they've gleaned from blogs and tabloids,
yes from gobby shites like me.
I'm a one-man munitions factory
in the biggest battle Britain's seen for bloody years
and all the while my mystery valet stalks my every utterance,
a steady spray of bullets from his Messerschmitt,
my Spitfire doing loop-the-loops,
attracting all those eyes.

I'm freelancing for real papers now:
The Guardian, *New Statesman*,
funny bits in *Metro*,
little slots on telly.
I'm having a good war,
battle-hardened,
raffish in the BBC green rooms.

Still Megan doesn't want to toast my triumphs.
Martyred to her maudlin commute,
she pours what little she has left in Suzy

and talks to me in sad, pugnacious sighs.
I wander woozy-wounded from my white-hot war
to snow drifts in the flat,
flinched cheek-pecks, short shrift replies
and I'm-not-sure-when-I'll-be-back-all-right.

She doesn't even mention Southend now.
Instead she leaves prospectuses for houses on the side.
And so I do the same with all my clippings,
sit there on the half-bought couch
long after Megan's gone to bed,
lost in the aftermath of news,
shooting bile from my bony thumbs,
and think about the hours on the road I used to do,
the articles I wrote for nothing,
years of being ignored at Edinburgh,
and now the thing was finally kicking off
my wife resented it, resented me,
was desperate to make me move away.
I gave her back her time at work.
I took the fucking childcare on.
Where is the compromise? I scream
and fantasise about a different life —

a study in a flat all of my own,
a place to be alone with all this rage.
I let myself imagine it;
what if Megan never came back home?

How has it come to this?
We have to make some joy again.
And so, I find a babysitter
and ask my wife out on a date.
"Yeah," she says, "I think that's what we need."

§

And it's tonight.
I ping my column off to Lucas,
Megan fills the babysitter in
and then we get the Tube
and it's kind of going well
but we try to get a cocktail and it's heaving,
we can't hear each other,
then everywhere we want to eat is booked
or queues snake out the door
and both of us are trying far too hard,

false breeziness — *Oh never mind, we could try...* —
nervous first-date awkwardness.

Eventually we're sitting in Wahaca
on a table by the toilets
and it's fucking loud and grating
and our conversation's drying
and the bloke whose back's to Megan's
got his legs stretched out and braying
in a public-schoolboy patois
to a brace of fellow wankers
till she's hunched into our table
and she's trying to tell me something
when this yawling pinstripe blurts out,
"Logan Dankworth's thing on Michael Gove!
That cracked me up!"

I perk up at the mention of my name.
"Just one sec, love, I want to hear this, yeah?"
There was a time we might have made a game of this,
conduct a running commentary of glances.
She looks down at her barely-touched fajita.
"Shall we go?"

It's muggy on the street outside.
We're walking out of sync.
I try to catch her hand, but Megan pulls away.
"Look, those guys were pricks," I start,
but when she stops and looks at me
I see we're miles apart.

"We're in real trouble, Logan.
Yes! It's fucking awful.
Surely you must see that.
You barely say a word to me these days.
Something needs to change...

You haven't even heard me out
You never ask me anything!
No, I don't give a shit about your work;
I'm not prepared to be an audience
to you if you won't hear me back.
I just don't think you get it.
These trains are fucking killing me."

And from the kerb the city
spills away from me,

the secret Soho bars,
the BBC and Black Lane Coffee Co.,
the shortcuts through The Green
and everything I've built myself upon.

Strangers are quoting me in restaurants.
I've never felt more London in my life
but there she is — that frankness in her eyes — my wife!
All plaintive and imploring in the setting sun of Soho
and I don't know what to do.

"I just need you to hear me, Logan."

And then my phone starts buzzing and instinctively I answer.
"Sorry, sorry... Lucas, I can't talk..."

But Lucas on the phone is in a panic.
"You fucking will.
We've got a major fucking problem..."

Megan's full of anger now;
it surges through her torso and her arms chop out at me.
"I handed in the notice on the flat.

We got a letter; they were gonna put the rent up
and I knew that if I told you you'd just pay it.
We're gonna rent in Southend, me and Suzy,
and if you want to join us there... you can."

§

Next day
in Black Lane Coffee Co.
Megan fills my thoughts.
I hated her last night.
My anger came from deep inside my bones
and coursed through my blood, my breath,
it choked me.
She threw away our home!

I watch a giant screen of rolling news.
Farage and Geldof, each on rival boats,
are facing off against each other on a sombre Thames.
I feel like a used-up blister pack.
I watch Sir Bob bark Euro facts
at Nigel through a megaphone:
You're no friend to the fisherman;

and, *You're a fraud;*
and, weirdly,
Get back to the river because you're up one without a canoe.

It doesn't help Bob's cause
that Nigel's got a slew of actual fishermen with him
who soak the meek Remainers with a hose.
In normal circumstances I'd be loving this;
it's half-baked, cock-eyed Britain at its best.
Today I find it bleak as fuck,
like awkward wedding fisticuffs.

The Battle of the Thames.
Years from now
they'll show this on a clip show of the decade.
The Battle of the Thames.
Is this what we've been fighting for?
Is this our Tiananmen?
Is *this* our Berlin Wall?
Lucas waddles in.

"Sorry Logan... coffee?"
I raise my paper cup.

"I know, that's why I offered.
Right, let's get down to it.
You've seen the article by now?"

I didn't call him back last night.
He texted though, a single line:
Tomorrow. Noon.

A thousand angry notifications flooded my screen.
Some *Daily Mail* hack had penned a piece
accusing me of writing Dankworth's Valet,
claiming it was all a ruse to gain some more publicity.
And in the age of fake news, instant rage and glanced appraisal,
I'd been tried on Twitter *in absentia*.

Cold sweat begins to trickle down my back.
I flit between my paper cup
and Nigel grinning on the deck
like Kaa from *Jungle Book*.

"We got our techy bloke on this last night."
He knows.

Let me explain...
Although I longed to fight
I found it hard to be so absolute.
My first attempts were over-qualified
and Lucas would have sacked me.
I could feel it coming at me,
Megan being sympathetic:
"Let's just start again in Essex."

I was desperate,
watching Suzy do her dialogue on the sofa,
then it hit me — split my arguments in two
to keep my columns marching straight.

It thrilled to write the opposite of what I thought
and I was bloody good at it.
Bewitched by my own rhetoric,
I put it up online
and called it Dankworth's Valet.

I preferred it even.
Logan Dankworth had to back things up,
defend the reasonable and sensible EU.

The Valet didn't.
He was there to tear the whole house down,
sweet oblivion, to bathe himself in anger and polemic,
pull the plug on torrents of abuse.

Lucas stares me down.
I'm squirming on the daggers in his eyes.
"I think we'll say you planned all this."

"But Lucas, mate, I didn't though."

"Yes, you fucking planned it,
it was brilliant
and I was in on it.
Comprende?"

My thoughts refuse to fall in place.

"This column's been a massive hit for us
and no one wants to lose all that,
so what we'll do is put the Valet on our site
and maybe introduce a few more characters.

I thought that we could call it
Downturn Abbey."

I stare at him.
"Yeah. I mean I get it.
But perhaps we could forget the Valet now.
The joke's been spoiled anyway.
I'd like to write more seriously for you.
Perhaps once all this EU stuff is settled, I could..."

Lucas shakes his head
and swipes my speech away.

"I don't think that you understand.
That path is closed to you.
No one's gonna trust you now.
The best that we can do is cast you as a prankster.
It's your only option, mate.
No one else will touch you with a bargepole."

His words seep into me.
He gathers up his stuff.

"Anyway I gotta go.
Apparently some bird's been shot up north.
It's fucking chaos out there!"

§

At home I watch Chief Constable Dee Collins,
sombre in her bobby's uniform,
starched white shirt and silver badge lapels.
She glances at her notes then speaks:

*Just before one o'clock today, Jo Cox, MP for Batley and
Spenborough, was attacked in Market Street, Birstall. I am
now very sad to report she has died as a result of her injuries.*

Megan's putting books in boxes on the floor.
She stops and scooches up to me.
She's being really nice,
even when I told her what I'd done.

"It's terrifying, innit...
You gonna sack it off?"

You said yourself, you want to write more seriously.
Take some time in Southend, get to know the place.
Work out what you want to do and
I'll take care of us."

I turn this over in my head,
imagining myself at home with Suzy,
pacing in my dressing grown
around a new-build semi.
But if I do what Lucas wants,
he'll get me off the hook.
I'll live to fight another day.

She's getting nervous at my silence.
"You're going to come with us though,
aren't you, Logan?"

§

And so to June the twenty-third.
Big Ben bongs
and Dimbleby begins:

At ten o'clock the polling stations close,
splitting passions, dividing friends.
Every vote will count as equal.

No exit polls to spoil the fun
although the pundits say REMAIN has won.
My guts are in agreement
and so it's perfect really,
the red crashing game of a fight,
but back home again for Christmas.

My troubles and my thoughts of Southend fade
as Laura Kuenssberg rattles off some gossip
and Jeremy Vine sweeps up a simulated Downing Street:
the blue line is for LEAVE
the yellow for REMAIN
and so we're off.

It's graduates v pensioners,
the cities v the shires,
little Englanders v worldly Scots,
and every vote will count they say again.
Every single vote will count —

every mad, disgruntled vote,

every disenfranchised vote,

every voter matters,

and the country is empowered,

as Nottingham and Sheffield and Mansfield light up blue.

England is a sea of it

with yellow desert islands leagues apart.

A minister looks lost, he says: *People don't believe us.*

Now all these little places

nibble at their moorings:

Craven, Kirklees, Ryedale, Selby,

Sandwell, Rugby, Tamworth, Lichfield,

Chelmsford, Harlow, Epping, Southend.

Farage beats his flabby chest

and struts around like Georgie Best.

Dare to dream, he cries at us.

This will be a victory for real people, decent people.

Am I not fucking real?

Are we not fucking decent?

Aren't we? Well?

What are we?

As from my iPhone Dimbleby declares:

The British people have spoken
and we're OUT.

§

"She has it into squares now."
Megan takes the plate away.

I sit down next to Suzy, dry her tears.
"We'll make some more," I whisper,
lightly tickle her beneath her chin.
She squirms and melts into my side.

I stroke her head and look down at my girl —
her dark blue polo shirt
and little cardigan,
the ribbons in her hair,
her perfect skin.

She's starting school today,
a little ship upon a boating lake,
while Megan and I sweat and heave
to keep the squall at bay.

It's ten weeks since the vote.
I come up here at weekends now,
occasionally a weeknight too.
I camp down in the spare room;
Megan often stays with friends.
She's got this group of mates down here.
She's cut her hair as well.
It's like she's moving on.
I hate this house she rents,
this semi in a cul-de-sac,
anonymous, a thousand miles from anywhere.
I can't live down here, but till I do
she doesn't want to talk.
She says she needs to see a leap of faith
but I'm not sure she'll catch me if I jump.
And so we're stranded, drifting on the blue.

At the school gate Megan holds her phone:
"Big smile, love!
Oh you look so grown up!"

"One of everyone!" says Suzy.
But Megan puts the phone away

and glances at her watch in phoney horror:
"Ooh no, you'll be late!"

We let the teacher lead her off.
She glances back at us and waves.

"Would it really hurt to have a photo all of us?"
Megan stares at me.

"You want to freeze these moments, Logan, really?
She's four, she doesn't care.
It breaks my heart to send her off when we're like this.
It's like you're weighing us up,
like, are we worth the move?
You're running out of time."

§

"She'll change her mind.
Southend will fucking wear her down," says Lucas,
tipping up his chemistry flask.
"Anyway, we need your fucking A game, yeah?"

We've got a meeting with some TV guys.
Since the vote I've built a cast of characters
to populate the columns that I write.
My massive staff of servants
each take turns to star:
my driver, Fernsby, thinks Saint Jez can do no wrong
and Mrs Briggs, the housekeeper,
is pushing for a people's vote.
She hides her sash at work just like a suffragette.

And then of course my valet;
he's the everyman who's got it wrong,
condemned to work for the worst kind of
avocado toast-scoffing millennial.
I drag him round to coffee shops with me
to plug my MacBook in.

I'm just another character in this
and everyone's a dickhead.

And now these guys
(there are two of them —
they're both called Andy)

want to make a sitcom of this world.

They join us at our table.
"Logan mate, we're pumped," says Andy One.
"We're really pumped," says Andy Two.
"Yeah, pumped, super pumped, pumped."

They nod in unison and credit where it's due:
they do seem pumped.
Even Lucas looks semi-inflated.

And this matey bonhomie is quite infectious,
certainly once they start reeling off
a list of all their projects, glittering and great.
Had I seen..?
And what about..?
And yes I had,
and obviously I loved it, didn't everyone?
"Logan, politics is fracturing
and no one sees that better than you do..."

My mind escapes its tether as they talk
and drifts away to BAFTAS, interviews...

I'd need to be in London for the filming.
Surely she would understand it now...

Andy One is talking at me while
my phone is buzzing in my pocket.
"Logan, mate, we need a page or two on this...."
It's Megan calling.
I screen it but she calls again.
I screen it but she calls again.

"I'm sorry, Andys, it's my wife..."
It's noisy on the street outside
and so I duck into an alleyway.
The smell of piss pervades my nose as Megan speaks.

"It's Suzy."
And then she starts to cry.

§

London disappears behind me
as I drive against the tide of morning rush-hour traffic.
Pylons stretch for miles across the dreary Essex marshes,

standing sentinel like bouncers.
If you're name's not down, you int coming in.
They straddle this expanse of nothingness
that leaves me feeling breathless, breathless.

Megan and I were the first of our friends to get married.
It felt so grown up, moving in together,
stripping off the paper, whitewashing the walls,
and when we'd kiss, all flecked with paint,
we'd brush our rings against the other,
let mine lightly catch on hers,
briefly hooked together.

She wasn't wearing hers last week.
It shocked me but I saw it by the sink;
I figured she'd been washing up.

I'm shunting in the stop-start snake of cars.
How's this place so busy now?
What even happens here?
I'm raging at the steering wheel.
I'm gripping it
then pinching it

until my fingers slide right off.
I'm slamming it in all my futile rage.

And in my mind's eye —
Suzy at the school gate,
all the education system looming over her,
weighing down on her.
It mixes with what Megan told me on the phone,
a truth I think we'd always known.

And when I finally get to school
I'm sweaty and I'm panicked and I'm late
and Megan's by the gate.
She smiles nervously
and takes my hand:
"It'll be all right."

§

We cram into the headteacher's office.
"I'm Jennifer," she says,
with kindness shot through every syllable.
Last year's whole school photo framed,

the tea towel that they get the kids to draw,
then photos of her own brood on her desk,
with gawky grins and echoes of their mum,
who fills the space in front of us and smiles, teeth and gums.

"Further to our conversation last week,
it's clear to us that Suzy's really struggling.
Now we are arranging an assessment, of course,
but as I say it's possible that she has ASD.
Autism Spectrum Disorder.
That she's autistic."

I try to focus in on all the acronyms
and leaflets being pushed across the table.

Megan's taking notes and asking questions.
"And what about an EHCP?
What's the SENCO's email?
Is that the Ed Psych report?
And how do you work the one-to-ones?
Thank you...
What are the assessment times?
Thank you...

And do you know any autism support groups?
Thank you.
Thank you.
Thank you."

§

Outside we take a moment on a wall,
a foot or two apart. We sit and breathe,
the yellow leaves around our feet.

"How come you knew so much about that stuff?"
I look across at her.
A car revs past.

"I looked it up," she says.
"Why, didn't you?"

"Sort of, it's been manic with the TV show...
Look. Things are fucking horrible, I know,
but all this stuff with Suzy sort of puts it in perspective, eh?"
She offers up an ink-black snort of laughter.
"I'm been an arse. I'm really sorry, Megan.

But we have to pull together now,
for Suzy's sake."

I trail off; it's terrifying.
Megan looks at me, then nods.
We almost share a smile.
It's like I've got a foot on solid ground.

"And what she said about the lack of funding —
I was half expecting that."

Now Megan turns to face me, warming up.
"Yes, yes, yes. The school don't want an EHCP
'cause they have to fund a lot of it themselves…"

"It's fucking unbelievable.
So, let's just sack them off
and look for schools in London.
We'll move wherever's best for her.
I don't mind living out a bit,
I'll take the hit and…"

"What? You're fucking kidding me."

I'll allow her that.
"I'm not.
She's obviously much better off in London.
They have the better teachers.
There's more money in the system."

She slowly shakes her head and looks away.
I'm on a landslide now; I'm slipping, sliding,
falling down, a hundred feet a second.
Megan speaks with steely clarity.

"First of all that's bollocks and
I've got support down here.
there's Mum and I've met friends.
She's settling in at school
and they've been brilliant.
They're the ones who noticed this..."

Her steel melts away.
She wipes a tear,
all four fingers of her right hand flat against her cheek,
so hard it pulls the skin.

"We always knew that something wasn't right.
No, no. I don't mean that...
There's nothing wrong with her,
she's perfect but...
I was scared to find out more
in case it wasn't her...
in case it's... all my fault."
The sob comes from her gut.
I shuffle up a little
and she crumples into me.
Our bodies heave together.

"I don't care," she says at last.
"If you can find a school in London, Logan...
I've got nothing left."

§

And now I'm really flying.
I was right. I saw it through
and she knows I was right.

Lucas calls:

"The Andys fucking love it.
We've got the BBC, then Channel 4 next week,
but I say we hold out for Sky.
There's much more money there."

I nod nod nod and pen more blogs
where everyone comes off as vile:
the shrill, elite Remaniacs,
the Gammons in the flat-roof pubs of Essex.
I don't care.
I tell myself the whole thing's fucking bullshit anyway.

I'm writing myself into the centre of the world.
I'm on and off the telly every week
and getting stopped in cafes, on the street.
I saw you stick it to that Owen Jones.
I saw you tell that Julia Hartley-Brewer.
Logan Dankworth — hello mate!

I'm tearing down their houses and it's easy,
slicing through their arguments like Schengen.
I've ceased to be on any side
and that is where my power lies.

And yes I find it hard to concentrate
on all the acronyms and forms
I have to read for Suzy
and these schools don't call you back
but that's ok,
we'll get there, yes, it's fine.

And then I get the call from *Question Time*.
They're doing it in Southend
and they want me as panelist.
"You live in Southend?" the producer asks.
"Yeah, yeah, yeah, we love it here."
I lie and laugh a little to myself.

§

And naturally I'm nervous round that curved, iconic table,
dazzled by the lights,
but Megan's in the audience, I know,
as David Dimbleby turns in his chair:

"Welcome to *Question Time*

which tonight comes from Southend."
The music plays, and all across the nation
Brits sit poised to bellow limply at the screen.

"And on tonight's panel..."

He reels off the names and accolades:
a Tory minister,
Remainer from the Labour front bench,
UKIP MEP,
a Lib Dem no one's heard of,
and then me: "Logan Dankworth, comedian and columnist
who's become the voice of Brexit Britain."

This is it, the centre of the storm.
I muscle in
and needle their hypocrisies:
the crumpled Tory Europhile
who found his inner sceptic
when Cabinet posts were being handed out;
the Labour centrist
(a pal of Owen Smith, no less)
who holds her nose to glad-hand up the pole;

the Liberal so called "Democrat"
who thinks we should ignore the people's will;
and, ugh, a UKIP MEP with those expenses claims —
"She's on the gravy Eurostar."

I flatten them with gusto,
bathe in laughter and applause.

But then this Lib Dem, Simon Mortimer,
he lands a blow:
"We know what you're against, Logan,
but what are you actually for?"

And if you watch this moment back
and freeze the frame,
you'll see it in my eye —
the truth of it.
Right then, I do not know
but sure enough I find some words to blurt:

"I'm for the British people."
Cue applause.
"I'm for improving lives and not just politicking."

Cue applause.

"My daughter goes to school in Southend.

She's autistic.

She won't get enough support at school,

not because the teachers don't care,

not because the expertise is lacking,

but there's just no money.

Our education system's crumbling."

Cue applause.

"Teachers being pushed to breaking point,

obsessed with tests and stats,

and little girls like Suzy pay the price.

So excuse me if it seems like I'm against you

when you sit there scoring points off one another,

but when you do, you waste my time

and what is more, you're wasting Suzy's too."

The crowd explodes;

there are people on their feet,

it's such a rush.

I feel it swell inside and push against my skin.

I want to burst.

§

And afterwards the green room is a joy.
My phone is buzzing, buzzing.
Lucas texts: *Tip-top, you fucking wanker.*
The editor stops by to say,
"We'd love to have you on again."
I beam with pride
and look around in vain for Megan.
Where is she?

Outside the night is violent and wet,
November howling out its truth
to anyone who'll hear.

I see her vaping in a shelter
perching on a metal hoop.
I bound across to her and call out,
but the moment that she looks at me
I know it's really bad.

"Pleased with your performance, are you, Logan?
I mean, they really fucking loved you, didn't they?

But where's this list of schools for Suzy?
Yeah, I thought as much.
You haven't done it.
It's been a month.
A fucking month.
You talk about our Suzy on telly
and they clap you.
Bravo, Logan Dankworth,
what a brilliant man —
if they could see the truth of it."

"You're the one who fucking left.
YOU ran away to Essex!"

"I wanted you to come!
I wanted us to build something together.
Live together. *Live.*
But you just couldn't see me for your own reflection.
What could I do to make you see?
I needed something real — a deed
that all your words could not undo."

I scrape my hair back off my forehead.

"You wouldn't fucking compromise!
I let you take the job."

"You let me?!
Don't you think I've compromised enough?
Look at yourself!
You shoot down everyone like it's a joke.
You blame the politicians
but at least they take a risk.
You only use the fight to further *you*.
No, don't, you've said enough.
Besides, I don't believe a word you say.
I don't trust you.

I fell in love with you because I saw you change.
To know that we can change
and we can change each other —
that is what I live for.

And I'm getting that in Southend, Logan.
I'm the real frontline.
You'll never change the world by shouting people down.
You have to meet them face to face;

you have to be prepared to let them change you too.

But I don't think you trust me either, do you?
Something happened to us,
after Suzy.
We stopped offering.
We started to demand.
And in the end I think
we just forgot how to be kind."

She's standing facing me,
that frankness in her grey-green eyes,
this strong and complex woman
that I thought I knew so well.

"It's over, isn't it?"

"I knew it on the wall outside the school.
I think that's why I let you take control.
I couldn't face the grief of knowing you were gone.

Take the car, I'll walk."
Megan holds my arm, and searches for my eyes.

"Suzy needs a lot from us.
I know you love her, Logan, but
you need to think about what kind of dad you want to be.
What kind of man.
Because, right now,
you're wasting our time."

§

That was three years ago.

Last night when I was driving home
I played the whole thing out again,
November howling out its dreadful truth.

I couldn't quell the fight in me.
The endless words that glut in my oesophagus.
I couldn't sate the need I had for glory
from this game, the biggest one that's played.

Another soldier with his dreams of medals.
I convinced myself that she was wrong.
I said I'm not the worst, no, it's the Brigadiers

who plot our path, protected by
their greater privilege, *they* order us:
Rees-Mogg reclining on the Commons bench
while Britain slides right off his rancid leg.

I told myself, I'm needed in the fight,
exhausted on my snatched weekends with Suzy.
Megan laying roots for both
of them as every month I drifted further off.

And everything I got I wanted more:
Remain v Leave or Right v Left,
ideologues in blinders baring sigils,
Euro stars or Union flag,
it doesn't matter which — we'd sooner split
ourselves in two than bow to compromise.

Like capital, enough will never be
enough: more cars, more roads,
more shopping malls, more raging violent rhetoric.
If that's your take, I'll better it. And on it went.
Words, words, words, more angry words,
colliding and producing steam, more smarting

people to divide, right down to their deadly atoms.

O, I watched my daughter changing from afar.
A deed that all my words could not undo.
That dreadful dawning as the days went by:
I was wrong and she was right.

I had to put my faith in Suzy, twist my shins
into the earth and let my daughter climb my branches,
so I packed my threadbare life into a van
and drove across the Essex marshes,
pylons standing sentinel,
and set up home in Southend.
But when I paced around my quiet house,
when nine o'clock came calling, how I played
that scene out in my head,
haunted by the offer Megan made —
work out what you want to do and I'll take care of us —
and how I'd turned away from her,
and how it was too late for us.

But not for me and Suzy.
I pick her up from school.

She's reading now,
learning to exist within her solitude.
It's beautiful...
I missed so much.

I'm trying, writing different things.
I've joined the PTA; I mostly listen.
I've found a little patch of peace.

Last night as I drove back home
I took the long way round, along the seafront,
parked the car and walked along the pier, a mile out.
Another far-flung corner of the country,
but I was there,
beneath my errors and my efforts and my choices,
breathing in the salty estuary,
and for a tiny moment I was
standing in the centre of the world.